Benjamin Birdie and the Tree Dwellers

Brown Books Kids
16250 Knoll Trail Drive, Suite 205
Dallas, Texas 75248
www.BrownBooksKids.com
(972) 381-0009

A New Era in Publishing®

Names: Dotsikas, Michael. | Spicer, Morgan, illustrator.

Title: Benjamin Birdie and the tree dwellers / written by Michael Dotsikas ; illustrated by Morgan Spicer.
Description: Dallas, Texas : Brown Books Kids, [2018] | Series: [Benjamin Birdie] ; [2] | Interest age level: 004-008. | Summary: "Benjamin Birdie, with his mother's support and encouragement from all his tree-dwelling friends, finds the courage and confidence to soar. Soon, after witnessing Benjamin's success, his tree-dwelling friends are inspired to follow their own dreams and try things they thought they could never do."-- Provided by publisher.
Identifiers: ISBN 9781612542768
Subjects: LCSH: Birds--Flight--Juvenile fiction. | Determination (Personality trait)--Juvenile fiction. | Confidence--Juvenile fiction. | CYAC: Birds--Flight--Fiction. | Determination (Personality trait)--Fiction. | Confidence--Fiction.
Classification: LCC PZ7.1.D68 Bet 2018 | DDC [E]--dc23

ISBN 978-1-61254-276-8
LCCN 2018937717

Printed in the United States
10 9 8 7 6 5 4 3 2 1

For more information or to contact the author, please go to
www.MichaelDotsikas.com.

To my mom—thank you for continually demonstrating the power of kindness.

To my wife, Dina—my perfect partner in this incredible journey; together we are making dreams come true.

To my children—follow your passions.

—Michael

Dedicated to the animals, my reason for being.

—Morgan

Acknowledgments:

Editor: Dina Dotsikas

Benjamin Birdie
and the
Tree Dwellers

Written By

Michael Dotsikas

Illustrated By

Morgan Spicer

KIDS

BROWN BOOKS KIDS

Benjamin Birdie had hoped for a flawless first flight, but it didn't go as planned; it just didn't go quite right.

Gazing out from his nest at the top of the tree,
he still yearned to fly far and still longed to fly free.

He continued to dream of his first "**real**" flight in the sky
and how high he would soar and how far he would fly.

And although he had **tumbled**
straight down to the ground,
he was ever so thankful for
the friends he had found.

The gibbons below
still didn't make a peep,
not to wake up the owls
who-o-o were **still** fast asleep.

The sloth was **still**
s-l-o-o-o-o-o-o-w,
and the kinkajou **still** small.

The cuscus clung tighter,
still afraid he might fall.

The porcupine was
still prickly,
the snake **_still_** spun
out of control,

while the howler monkey
still screamed
s-o-o-o-o-o-o-o-o-o-o
much louder than all.

And . . .

Benjamin Birdie was ***still*** not ready to fly, although more anxious than ever to give it a try.

He counted the hours . . . the days . . . and the weeks,

staring out at **vast** valleys,

broad brooks,

and ꞇall peaks.

Till early one morning on this one **special** day,
Mama Birdie returned from a short time away.

"You're now a bit older; your wings have grown **strong**.
Your *someday* has come! You have waited so long."

"Get ready, my son, and spread well-earned wings.
It's time to accomplish some ***wonderful*** things!"

But . . .

Benjamin Birdie didn't know how to feel.
Could he be dreaming? Could this be real?

At the ground
f-a-a-a-a-a-a-a-r-r-r
below, he nervously stared.
Although anxious to fly,
he was now somewhat
SCARED.

Benjamin leapt off the branch with a spirited bound and was flying quite nicely till he glanced at the ground.

He suddenly felt a deep plunge in his belly; his heart beat much faster, and his wings turned to

jelly.

While *flipping* and *flopping*
and *flailing* around,
he happened to hear an
encouraging sound.

His tree-dwelling friends—
quite a boisterous crowd—
were cheering him on,
ever proudly and loud.

Benjamin's frown swiftly
turned upside down
as he skillfully stopped his
descent to the ground.

"I'm flying! I'm flying!" he hollered out loud.
"Look, Mama, **I did it!** I hope you are proud."

He was dashing and darting
all through the tree.

He was hooting and howling,
"Now look at **M-E-E-E-E-E-E!**"

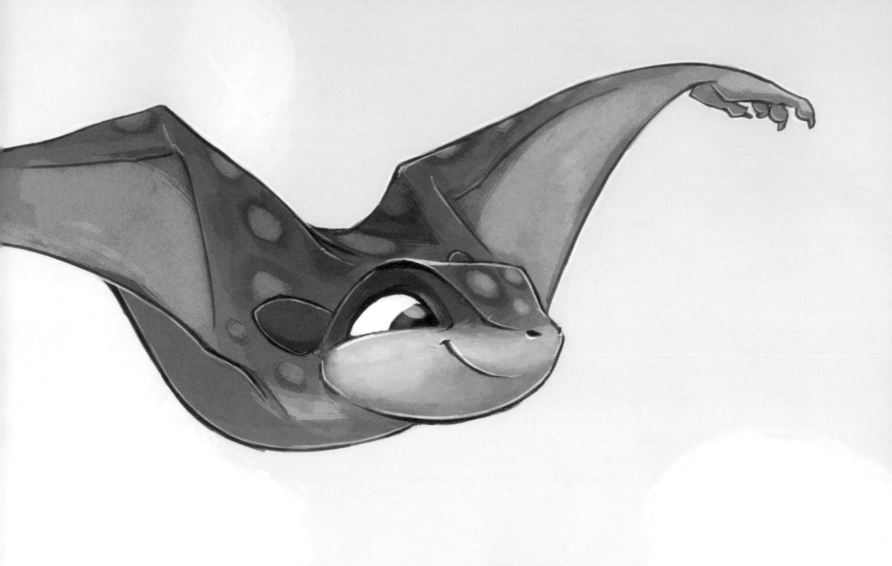

Benjamin Birdie, with wings spread out **WIDE**, expertly glided with friends by his side.

Soaring high with
the sparrows and

flying low with
the finches,

he missed colliding with
geese by just a **few inches!**

Whirling and twirling to a
neighboring tree,
Benjamin was zigging and zagging
like a crazed bumblebee.

The primates were dazzled
by this young bird's finesse.
The tamarin didn't show it,
but he too was impressed.

Benjamin was delighted
for new friends to meet,
greeting them warmly
with a smile and a tweet.

The
panda bears
huddled,

the
koala bears
cuddled,

while the bewildered
bearcats seemed
utterly **befuddled**.

The tree dwellers took notice
of **Benjamin's** success.
They were truly *inspired* and
extremely impressed.

They were now driven to
try something *new*,
something they once
thought they just couldn't do.

The elephant thought, if this bird could fly,
then once again he should give it a try.

He flapped his **HUGE** ears even faster and faster,
but flying was something he just could not master.

The gibbons had talents
they wanted to share:
clipping and styling the
tree dwellers' hair.

The jaguar tried juggling
along with the 'roo.
The snake was determined
to play the kazoo.

The flying squirrel
learned Spanish.

The sloth won a race!

The flying lemur prepared
for his journey in space.

Stage fright kept the cuscus from singing out loud
and afraid to perform in front of a crowd.

Seeing **Benjamin** soar caused a stirring sensation.
A new pop star was born to a rousing ovation!

The giraffe and the kinkajou were **ARTISTS** at heart,
but reluctant and bashful to exhibit their **ART**.

Benjamin's flight made their confidence rebound,
leaving their audience awed and spellbound.

Becoming a nurse was
the porcupine's dream.

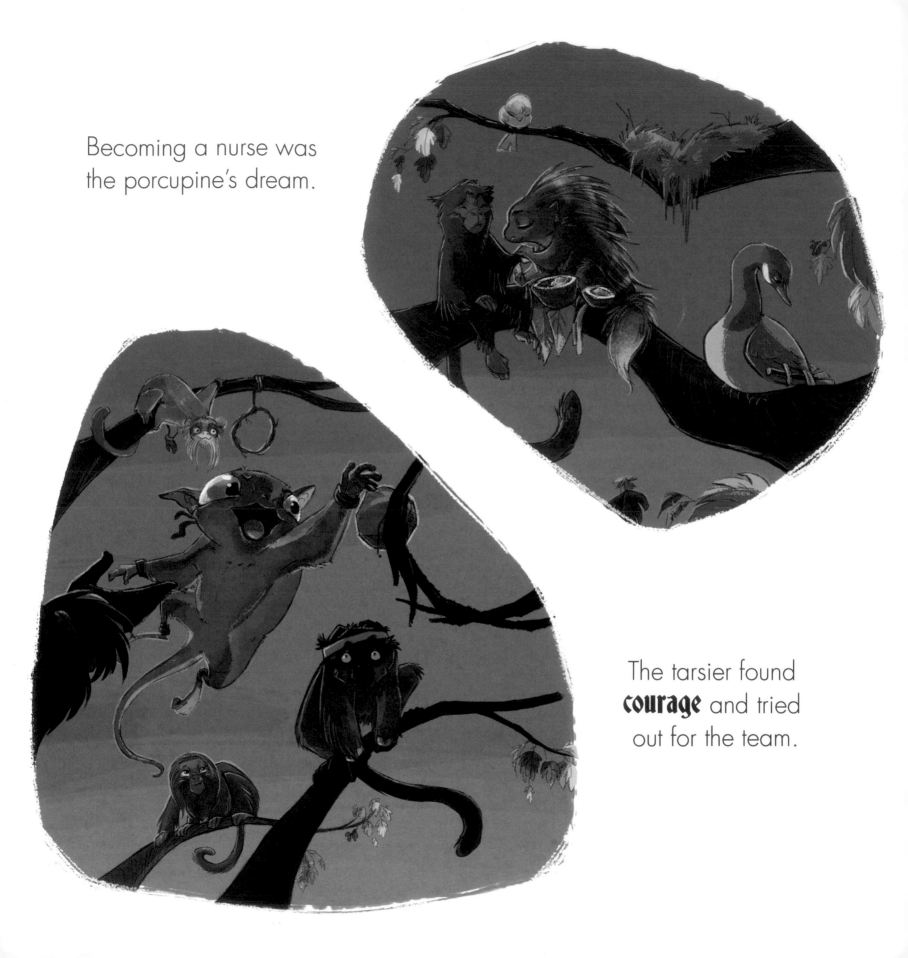

The tarsier found
courage and tried
out for the team.

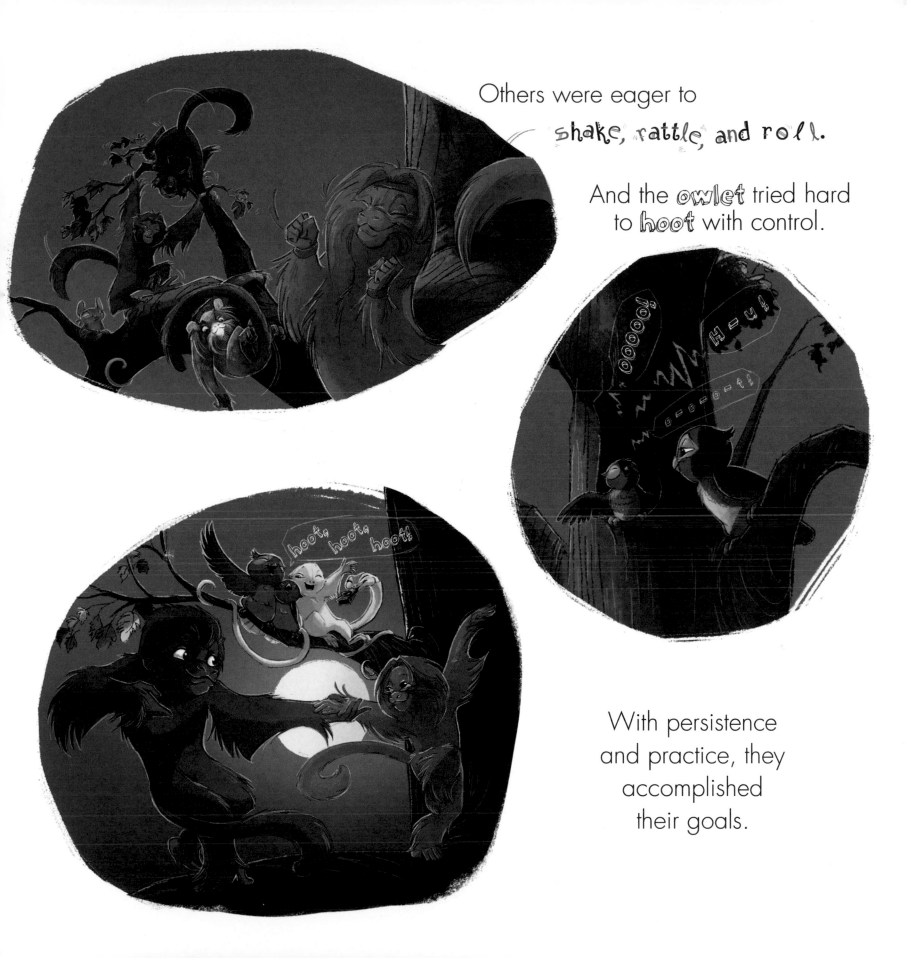

Others were eager to
shake, rattle, and roll.

And the owlet tried hard
to hoot with control.

With persistence
and practice, they
accomplished
their goals.

Some succeeded,
some failed, but all
held their heads high
cause what
mattered the most is
each gave it a try.

Benjamin Birdie inspired the tree dwellers in their own special way.

"Here's to our fabulous, feathered friend . . . .

hip, hip, **HOORAY!**"

Gazing out with excitement and yearning for more,

Benjamin Birdie was ready
for a world to explore.

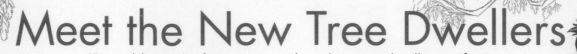

Meet the New Tree Dwellers

(For additional information on the other tree dwellers, refer to
Benjamin Birdie's First Flight – book #1 in the **Benjamin Birdie** Book Series)

Emperor Tamarin
[**em**-per-or **tam**-*uh*-rin, -ran]
(endangered in some regions)

The emperor tamarin is a small primate found in lowland tropical rainforests that can reach 10 inches in length and weigh up to 2 pounds. It is named after German Emperor Wilhelm II because of its long, droopy moustache. A diurnal mammal, the emperor tamarin spends most of its life in the trees and rarely descends to the forest floor. Emperor tamarins communicate via hissing sounds and chirping calls. When they have babies, they often give birth to twins, with other family members helping to raise the babies.

Red Howler Monkey
[red **hou**-ler **muhng**-kee]
(vulnerable in some regions)

The largest of the species, red howler monkeys averaging 20 individuals. Their long, and their hands are and dexterous. They usually remain where they can find the most leaves, primary source of food. Although they rain forests, they do not like rain and protest to rainstorms. Red howler monkeys mischievous animals who sit high in trees and pester jaguars throwing sticks and branches down at them. The least active of all monkeys, they spend the majority of their time relaxing—they sleep for more than 15 hours per day!

howler mon live in troops arms and legs extremely strong high up in trees which is their live in tropica will howl in are very

Panda Bear
[**pan**-d*uh* bair]
(vulnerable)

Panda bears, also known as giant pandas, are solitary mammals found only in thick, wet bamboo forests, high up in the mountains of central China. They grow to 5 feet tall and weigh up to 300 pounds. As omnivores, they will occasionally eat small animals and fish, but 99 percent of their diet consists of bamboo. Every day they eat for up to 12 hours, consuming up to 28 pounds of bamboo! Pandas have a special bone that extends from their wrists called a "pseudo-thumb," which they use to hold and manipulate bamboo. The walls of their stomach are extra muscular to digest the wood of the bamboo and are covered with mucus that prevents it from being punctured by splinters. Baby pandas are born pink and measure about 6 inches— the size of a pen! Born blind, pandas open their eyes six to eight weeks after birth. Unlike most other bears, pandas do not hibernate. As winter approaches, they head lower down the mountain to warmer temperatures.

Koala
[koh-**ah**-luh]
(protected)

Koalas are nocturnal marsupials that live on eucalyptus trees and measure 25 to 30 inches long and weigh 20 to 30 pounds. Their name comes from an Aboriginal term meaning *"no drink,"* because koalas rarely drink water and get almost all their moisture from the leaves they eat. A koala's diet consists of leaves from the eucalyptus tree, which are tough and poisonous! Luckily, koalas have a cecum—a long digestive organ—which allows them to break down the leaves unharmed. Koalas don't have much energy and usually sleep for up to 19 hours a day. When they're not sleeping, they communicate with each other through burping and snoring noises! When koalas are born they are only half an inch long—about the size of a jellybean! Koalas have two thumbs on their front paws that help them climb, hold on to the tree branches, and grip their food.

The bearcat, also known as the binturong, is a small-sized nocturnal mammal (2 to 3 feet long and an average weight of 48 pounds) found only in dense tropical rain forests. It has a face that looks like a cat and a body shaped like a bear; however, it is not related to either animal. Bearcats live high in the forest canopy and rarely come down to the ground. They are excellent climbers, aided by a thick prehensile tail and strong feet with semiretractable claws. Although bearcats are carnivores, they mostly eat fruit, especially apples, bananas, and their favorite—grapes! Bearcats always smell "yummy," as their scent glands emit a unique odor that smells like buttered popcorn!

Monk Parakeet
[muhngk **par**-uh-keet]
(least concern)

Bearcat
[**bair**-kat]
(vulnerable)

The monk parakeet is an extremely intelligent species of parrot named for the markings on its head, which are said to resemble a monk's hood. These small parrots (11 to 12 inches long) can be found all over the world, inhabiting dry, semiopen woodland and savanna. They also adapt well to urban areas. Known as talking birds, they have an excellent ability of imitating speech. In Spain, they have become a tourist attraction, living in the trees near Gaudi's Sagrada Familia basilica and speaking Spanish to spectators. A very sociable species, they stay in large, noisy flocks of around 30 to 50 individuals. Unlike other parrot species, monk parakeets build stick nests rather than nesting inside hollow spaces.

Canada Goose
[**kan**-uh-duh goos]
(least concern)

Tree snails are mollusks, closely related to other snails and slugs, and are found all over the world, usually in warm and humid tropical regions. They dwell on the trunk, stem, and leaves of trees. Moving slowly over short distances, tree snails feed on fungus, which they sense using olfactory cues. Most tree snails share the same physical characteristics: colorful, spiral-shaped shells and antenna-like stalks on the top of their heads, which are actually their eyes.

Tree Snail
[tree sneyl]
(several species are **endangered**)

The Canada goose is a migratory bird species that flies south for the winter to warmer climates in search of food, following the same flying routes every year. They migrate in large groups called flocks, flying in an aerodynamic "V formation" which helps them conserve energy while flying long distances—as they can sometimes cover over 1,000 miles in just 24 hours! A Canada goose male, called a gander, can weigh up to 14 pounds with a wingspan of up to 5 feet. A typical clutch, incubated solely by the female, consists of 4 to 7 eggs. The gander's job is to protect the nest. A gander is a fierce defender of his mate and offspring, charging any animal that threatens his family—even animals as large as elk!

Glossary

Aboriginal – relating to or characteristic of the native peoples of Australia

aerodynamics – the qualities of an object that affect how easily it is able to move through the air

bamboo – any of various woody or treelike grasses of tropical and temperate regions having thick, hollow stems that are used for food

carnivore – an animal that eats meat

clutch – a group of chicks

consume – to eat or drink in great quantity

descend – to pass, move, or climb down or down along

dexterous – skillful, graceful, and competent

diurnal – active mainly during the day

eucalyptus – mostly Australian evergreen trees that have rigid entire leaves and umbrella-shaped flowers, cultivated for their gums, resins, oils, and woods

forest canopy – the highest layer of branches in a forest or on a tree

hibernate – to spend the winter sleeping or resting

incubate – to sit on eggs so as to hatch by the warmth of the body

marsupial – an order of mammals (kangaroos, wombats, bandicoots, opossums, koalas, and related animals) that usually have a pouch on the abdomen of the female that serves to carry the young

migratory – traveling from one place to another at regular times of year, often over long distances

mischievous – showing a playful desire to cause trouble

mollusk – invertebrate animals (such as snails, clams, or squids) with a soft, unsegmented body usually enclosed in a calcium shell

mucus – a slippery, thick, sticky substance that moistens and protects the linings of body passages and spaces (as of the nose, lungs, and intestines)

olfactory – concerned with the sense of smell

omnivore – an animal that eats both plants and other animals

pseudo – not genuine; fake

savanna – a tropical or subtropical grassland containing scattered trees and drought-resistant undergrowth

scent gland – a cluster of cells or an organ in the body that produces a substance with a strong odor that plays a part in animal communications

troop – a group of monkeys

For additional glossary words, refer to **Benjamin Birdie's First Flight** – book #1 in the **Benjamin Birdie** Book Series. (Visit our website at www.michaeldotsikas.com/benjaminbirdieandthetreedwellers for citations and references.)

Also by **Michael Dotsikas** and **Morgan Spicer**:

Benjamin Birdie's First Flight
(Book #1 in the **Benjamin Birdie** Series)

Kirkus Reviews: "An endearing adventure with verse that soars!"

Readers' Favorite five-star review: "Masterpiece, a must read for children and adults."

IndiReader: "The rhyming scheme and the story are endearing and engaging, and the lovable expressions of the animals and the muted earth tones of the vintage-style illustrations are captivating."